Magical mayhem

Kitty Wells

David Fickling Books
OXFORD · NEW YORK
31 Beaumont Street
Oxford OX1 2NP, UK

POCKET CATS 8: MAGICAL MAYHEM
A DAVID FICKLING BOOK

978 1 849 92032 2

Published in Great Britain by David Fickling Books,
a division of Random House Children's Books
A Random House Group Company

This edition published 2011

1 3 5 7 9 10 8 6 4 2

The Random House Group Limited supports the Forest Stewardship Council (FSC), the leading international forest certification organization. All our titles that are printed on Greenpeace-approved FSC-certified paper carry the FSC logo. Our paper procurement policy can be found at www.rbooks.co.uk/environment.

Typeset in 16/20 Times by Falcon Oast Graphic Art Ltd.

DAVID FICKLING BOOKS
31 Beaumont Street, Oxford, OX1 2NP

www.**kidsatrandomhouse**.co.uk
www.**rbooks**.co.uk

Addresses for companies within The Random House Group Limited can be found at: www.randomhouse.co.uk/offices.htm

THE RANDOM HOUSE GROUP Limited Reg. No. 954009

A CIP catalogue record for this book is available from the British Library.

Printed and bound in Great Britain by CPI Bookmarque, Croydon.

The *Pocket Cats* series is dedicated to all cat lovers, everywhere . . . including you!

Chapter One

Maddy Lloyd breathed deeply as she got out of the car. The air in the seaside town of Torton was just as she remembered: a fresh, salty breeze that tickled her nose and ruffled her long brown hair. Overhead, seagulls screamed as they wheeled and dipped in the sky.

"Yay, we're here!" cried Maddy's best friend Rachel, bouncing out of the car on the other side. Her glasses were crooked, and she straightened them with an impatient shove.

Rachel's Aunt Tilly smiled as she climbed out of the driver's seat. Her short, spiky red hair looked like an explosion. "It's been a while, eh, girls?"

It was the Easter break, and Maddy was staying with Rachel and her Aunt Tilly. She'd stayed with Rachel and her aunt once before, but that had only been for a weekend. This was for a whole week – seven blissful days of helping out in Aunt Tilly's quirky shop, and exploring the beach, and sniffing the fresh sea air. Maddy could hardly wait!

"Everything looks just the same," she said happily as she and Rachel carried their suitcases towards Tilly's Treasures, the antique shop on the

High Street that Aunt Tilly owned.

Aunt Tilly's bracelets jangled as she unlocked the shop door. "Almost," she said, nodding at a shop across the road. "There's a newcomer, as you can see!"

Maddy peered curiously at the new shop. There were great swaths of purple velvet draped in its window,

MAGICAL
MYSTERIES

with a crystal ball sitting on top of them. A brightly coloured sign said, *Magical Mysteries. Psychic Readings, Ghostbusting and General Magical Advice. No job too small!*

"Wow, there's a *psychic* there now?" asked Maddy. She knew that psychics were people who claimed they could tell the future.

"*General Magical Advice*," read Rachel. "I wonder what that means."

Aunt Tilly sniffed. "It means that Clarissa, my new neighbour, is full of tosh! There's no such thing as psychic powers, or magic. But she seems to have plenty of customers anyway. There's no limit to the foolishness some people will believe!"

Maddy and Rachel exchanged a secret smile as they followed Aunt

Tilly into the antique shop. As strange as it might seem, they both knew that there really *was* such a thing as magic! Right at that very moment, Maddy had hidden in her suitcase a set of three tiny ceramic cats. Though no one but herself and Rachel knew it, the cats could actually come to life if there was a problem that needed solving – and more than that, they could give Maddy amazing feline powers!

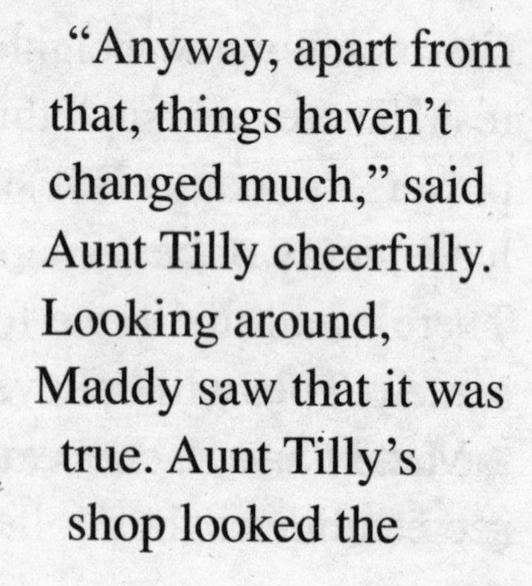

"Anyway, apart from that, things haven't changed much," said Aunt Tilly cheerfully. Looking around, Maddy saw that it was true. Aunt Tilly's shop looked the same as always: chock-full of fascinating things like Victorian birdcages, old jewellery and racks of vintage clothing. It was the sort of place you could lose yourself in for hours.

"Are we staying in the same room as last time, Aunt Tilly?" asked Rachel, tucking back a strand of her long blonde hair.

"Where else?" said her aunt with a smile.

"Come on, race you!" cried Rachel to Maddy. The two girls took off through the door marked PRIVATE, and

pounded up a flight of steep wooden stairs. Just as Maddy remembered, there were two little bedrooms upstairs, and a bathroom with a claw-foot bathtub.

The girls' bedroom had two single beds and a tiny round window like a porthole looking out over the High Street, with a view of the sea just beyond. Dropping their suitcases, the two friends pressed together in front of it, staring out happily at the waves.

"It's so great to be back!" said Maddy, nudging Rachel with her arm. "We're going to have such a brilliant week."

Rachel grinned. "I almost burst out laughing when Aunt Tilly said that about magic!" Glancing at the open doorway, she lowered her voice.

"Did you bring them?"

Maddy nodded. "Of course!"

Delving into her suitcase, she brought out a carefully wrapped parcel made from a red silk handkerchief. Placing it on the dressing table, she gently unwrapped the handkerchief's folds. As the silk fell away, three tiny ceramic cats came into view, their paws and tails entwined: chunky, wise Greykin; sleek, black Nibs; and Ollie, with the laughing amber eyes.

Maddy's smile became wistful as she regarded the cats. It had been months since Greykin had last come to life. Next it would be Nibs's turn, and Maddy longed to see the matter-of-fact little cat again – but when?

Rachel sighed as if she were thinking the same thing. "I suppose you can't really tell with magic," she said. Joining Maddy at the dressing table, she propped her chin on her hand. "It'll happen when it's ready to, and not a moment before."

"Well, I hope it's not much longer," said Maddy as she started to unpack the rest of her things. "And it *must* be almost time for the magic again, don't you think? It's been ages!"

Rachel shook her head. "That's not very scientific, Maddy," she chided.

Maddy hid a smile. Her best friend was extremely logical, even about things like magic!

"There's just no telling when one of the cats might come to life again," Rachel went on. "It could happen tomorrow, or next month, or next year."

Maddy froze with a pile of T-shirts in her hands. "Next *year*?" she echoed in horror. "But I don't want to wait until then!"

"It probably won't be that long," said Rachel hastily. "I'm just saying that logically, it *could* be."

Maddy put her T-shirts away glumly. She didn't think very much of logic, if that was the case! She'd rather believe that the magic would happen again soon. But what if Rachel were right? Even worse . . . what if the magic never happened again? It had been so long already.

The thought was too awful to say out loud. Maddy gazed anxiously at the cats. The ceramic trio stared back at her with painted feline smiles that gave away nothing at all.

"Would you girls like to come with me this afternoon?" asked Aunt Tilly as they ate lunch in the little kitchen behind the shop. "I'm going to a local auction, to see if there's anything worth bidding on."

"You mean to sell here in the shop?" asked Rachel.

Aunt Tilly nodded. "It's an estate sale – that means that it's what was in someone's house. There's supposed to be a lot of vintage clothing, and some antique furniture that I want to take a look at."

"Do you want to?" Rachel asked Maddy, and Maddy nodded eagerly. She'd never been to an auction before, though she'd seen them on TV – where, if you weren't careful, just accidentally touching your nose might mean that you'd bought a priceless painting! She supposed auctions weren't like that in real life, though, or else nobody would ever go to them.

The girls ran upstairs to use the loo and put on their shoes before leaving.

Brushing her hair at the dressing table, Maddy hesitated as she looked down at the cats. On impulse, she tucked the ceramic Nibs into her jeans pocket. The cat's small, cold figure felt comforting as she touched it.

With a smile, she pounded down the stairs again. Maybe Rachel was right, and it would take months for Nibs to come to life again – but she wanted to be prepared, just in case!

The auction took place in a large warehouse-type building, crammed full of long tables covered with goods. "That's what I want to look at – all that lovely vintage clothing!" said Aunt Tilly with a gleam in her eye. She headed over to some tables in the corner, where coats and dresses were on display.

On their own, the two girls drifted down the rows of tables. Each item up for auction had a tag with a number on it. Rachel consulted the brochure. "Ooh, look, there are antique books somewhere!" she cried, her eyes

ng up. "Maddy, do you want to come and see?"

"In a minute," said Maddy. She had spotted a dusty cardboard box that had all sorts of things in it: a broken clock, a pair of silver-plated candlesticks, a dented napkin ring . . . "Rachel, what does the brochure say about this box?"

Her friend made a face. "It *should* say, *Box of old junk* . . . No, it says, *Lot 62: Assorted items from the Fletcher estate*. Sure you won't come and see the books?"

"You go on, I'll catch you up," said Maddy, rummaging through the box. For some reason, it had taken hold of her interest, so that it was impossible for her to just walk away from it. It felt almost as if she had lost something, and was trying to find it again.

"OK, see you soon," said Rachel, heading off to another table.

Maddy delved more deeply, pushing aside an ancient cuddly rabbit and an old cigar box. *Why* was she so interested in all this stuff? She didn't know, but suddenly it seemed very urgent that she keep searching. She had to find whatever it was . . . she *had* to . . .

Then Maddy gasped, her hands flying up to her cheeks as a prickling feeling raced across them. Just as if she had invisible whiskers, which were now quivering with excitement!

"The magic!" whispered Maddy, her heart thudding. It was back! Whenever there was a problem to be solved that needed cat magic, she got a tingling feeling where her whiskers would be, if she were a cat. And now the sensation was growing stronger by the second, the magic pounding through Maddy's veins like a drumbeat. No wonder she'd felt so keen to look through this box – somewhere in here was the problem that needed solving!

Automatically her hand went to her jeans pocket. Nibs's small body was still cold and smooth. So Maddy hadn't found whatever the problem was yet, but she knew she must be very close – her whiskers were still tingling like mad!

Excitedly Maddy pushed aside the last few items . . . and gazed at the box's cardboard bottom in confusion. "Where is it?" she muttered, pawing through the items again. The problem *must* be in here – she could feel it!

Then she spotted a slim golden chain, half hidden under a flap of the box's cardboard bottom. Pouncing on it, she drew it out – and found herself staring at an old-fashioned oval locket. It had a tiny garnet set in its centre, and two initials engraved on it: JM.

She stared at the locket as it dangled from her fingertips. Something to do with this locket was the problem, she was sure of it!

"Excuse me, little girl, can I have a look?" said an impatient voice beside her. Turning, Maddy found herself face to face with a large woman wearing a pink flowery top. Without waiting for Maddy to answer, she pulled the box towards her.

"Yes, sorry," mumbled Maddy. Reluctantly she placed the locket back in the box. The woman moved closer, forcing Maddy to step away. Agonized, she kept her gaze on the locket, watching as it slithered down amongst the other items.

The woman glanced idly at it, and then her eyes lit up as she saw the silver-plated candlesticks. "How lovely!" she murmured, reaching for them. "Oh, I'll have these, if I can!"

"Excuse me," burst out Maddy. "If – if there's something that you want to buy, what do you do?"

"You bid for it, of course," said the woman, still inspecting the silver candlesticks. "If you bid more than anyone else, then you win."

Maddy glanced up at the podium, where a man wearing round spectacles looked as if he were about to begin. She only had a few pounds with her. What if she couldn't afford to buy the box with the locket in it? How would she be able to solve the problem?

All at once Maddy felt a familiar, warm stirring in her pocket. Her spirits lifted in a rush. Nibs had come to life!

Chapter Two

Maddy raced towards the loo, grabbing Rachel on her way. "Come on!" she hissed, tugging at her friend's arm.

Rachel looked up, blinking, from an antique book. "What is it?"

There were people all around them. "Just *hurry*!" urged Maddy, widening her eyes significantly.

Rachel's own eyes grew round as she suddenly understood. "Oh!" she gasped, dropping the book. The two girls ran for the privacy of the loos, quickly closing themselves into a stall together. Thankfully, no one else was in there – everyone was gathering for the beginning of the auction.

"Has it happened again? Has it really happened?" whispered Rachel eagerly.

"I assume you're talking about me," said a dry voice from Maddy's pocket.

With a grin, Maddy put her hand in her pocket, feeling Nibs's sleek warmth. The little cat stepped tidily onto her palm, and Maddy held her up. "Oh, Nibs, you're back!" she squealed, cuddling her against her cheek.

"Well, that's fairly obvious, isn't it?" said Nibs. But her purr gave away her true feelings as she rubbed her face against Maddy's. Nibs was every bit as glad to see her as she was to see Nibs!

"Hi, Nibs," breathed Rachel, carefully stroking the cat's tiny back with her fingertip. Though Nibs had taken time to warm to Rachel, the two were now firm friends. "It's *so* good to see you again."

"Yes, it's good to be back,"

admitted Nibs, sitting perched on Maddy's palm. Gazing at her, Maddy thought that she looked like a tiny panther – all midnight black, apart from her bright green eyes. "But *where* are we?" Nibs added, looking around the stall and wrinkling her nose.

Maddy quickly explained, her words tumbling over each other.

"A locket, eh? Interesting," mused Nibs, the tip of her tail twitching. "Well, you'll have to bid for it. We must have that locket!"

Maddy nodded, feeling worried. "I only have a few pounds, though."

"I've got ten pounds," put in Rachel. "You can have it, if you like." Maddy squeezed her friend's hand gratefully. She knew that Rachel had probably been planning to bid on one of the dusty books she'd been looking at.

"Right, we'd better go – the auction's about to start," said Maddy, looking at her watch. In response, Nibs padded quickly up her arm and settled on her shoulder, where she was hidden behind a curtain of long brown hair. Maddy grinned. It had been so long since she'd had a tiny cat riding about on her shoulder; she'd forgotten how amazing it felt!

"Oh, Nibs, I'm *so* glad you're back!" she burst out, scratching the cat's head with a single fingernail.

Nibs purred again, rubbing her head against Maddy's finger. Then she stopped and cleared her throat. "No time for sentiment," she said briskly.

"Come on – we've got a locket to bid on!"

Bidding turned out to be more complicated than Maddy had thought. You had to register your name with a man at the front, who gave you a thing like a fan to hold up when you wanted to make a bid.

"Is there an adult with you?" he asked doubtfully when Maddy tried to register.

Thankfully, Aunt Tilly turned up just then. "Yes, me," she said, putting her hand on Maddy's shoulder. "She can bid, if she likes."

Maddy blew out a sigh of relief

as the man put her name down and handed her a fan like the others. "Thanks, Aunt Tilly," she whispered.

Aunt Tilly raised an eyebrow at her as they went to their seats. "Found something you like?"

Maddy glanced at the cardboard box, which was now sitting up at the front with the other items in the auction. "Sort of – I mean, it's just a box full of old things, but—"

"Say no more!" laughed Aunt Tilly. "Believe me, I know the appeal of old things. That's why I have an antique shop!"

Despite her nervousness, Maddy watched with interest as the auction began. The auctioneer started by describing each item and suggesting a sum, and then people put their fans in the air, faster and faster as the amount increased. Whenever someone won something, the auctioneer banged his gavel down on the podium and said, "Sold!" Some things went for lots of money, some for only a few pounds. Maddy began to feel hopeful. Maybe she could afford the box with the locket in it after all.

On her shoulder, Nibs seemed interested as well. Maddy could feel the little cat sitting up, peering through her hair. "I don't see why *that* went for so much," she sniffed in Maddy's ear as a painting was sold. "It's just a bunch of swirls and blobs!"

"It's called modern art," murmured Maddy under her breath. She agreed with Nibs, though. The painting looked like something she could have done herself, and she was dreadful at art.

She held back a giggle as Nibs's whiskers tickled her ear. "Well, give me old-fashioned art then. Honestly, you humans!"

Finally the cardboard box came up for bid. Maddy sat up in her seat, her heart pounding. She and Rachel exchanged excited, anxious looks.

"Lot sixty-two, a box of various items from the Fletcher estate," announced the man. "Bidding will start at five pounds. Am I bid five pounds?"

Maddy lifted her fan in the air. *Please, don't let anyone else bid!* she thought fervently.

The man pointed at her. "Five pounds from the little lady. Will I see ten?"

AUCTION
TODAY

Instantly the woman in the flowered top put her fan up. Glancing across the room at her, Maddy felt nervousness prickle across her scalp. The woman looked very determined!

"Ten pounds . . . ten pounds . . . Any advance? Will I see fifteen?"

Fifteen pounds? Dismay swept through Maddy. Even with Rachel's money, she only had twelve! Was it over already?

"Go on, what are you waiting for?" hissed Nibs.

"I don't *have* fifteen pounds," Maddy muttered back, feeling close to tears. Then she gasped in surprise as Aunt Tilly took hold of her arm, raising her fan.

"I'll give you a few pounds," she whispered cheerfully. "This is exciting, isn't it?" She'd already won several lots of vintage clothing that she'd wanted, and was in a good mood.

"Oh, thank you!" gasped Maddy. "I'll pay you back, I promise!"

The auctioneer pointed his gavel at her. "Fifteen pounds from the little lady. Very nice . . . Will I see twenty?"

The lady in the flowered top gave Maddy a cold look as she put her fan up again.

"Twenty pounds . . . twenty pounds. Will I see twenty-five?" The auctioneer peered at Maddy expectantly. The audience was watching her too, looking very amused.

Maddy hardly noticed. She bit her lip as she glanced at Aunt Tilly, who nodded. "Yes, but this is as high as we go," she warned.

Her heart thudding, Maddy put her fan in the air. The man pointed at her.

"Twenty-five pounds from the little lady – will I see thirty, madam?"

Maddy twisted in her seat to look at the lady in the flowered top. With a scowl, the woman hesitated, her lips tight. Bouncing on the seat next to Maddy, Rachel clutched her arm. "I think you've got it!" she whispered.

"Going once to the little lady . . . going twice . . ."

Happiness rushed through Maddy.

Oh, phew! She'd been so worried, but now she'd be able to solve the problem of the locket after all! Then her blood ran cold as the woman lifted her chin stubbornly and thrust her fan up in the air. *No!*

"Thirty pounds!" cried the auctioneer. "Will I see thirty-five?"

"Sorry, lovey – I think you're going to have to do without it," said Aunt Tilly in an undertone. Maddy nodded mutely. She knew that she couldn't expect Aunt Tilly to spend so much money, but – oh, what was she going to do now?

"Going once . . . going twice . . . *sold*, for thirty pounds!" announced the auctioneer, banging his gavel. "Sorry, my dear," he added to Maddy with a fatherly wink. The audience chuckled, but Maddy didn't even try to smile. She watched glumly as the box was taken away to another room.

From Maddy's shoulder, Nibs huffed out a breath. "Oh, this won't do at all!" muttered the little cat. "Excuse me."

And before Maddy could react, Nibs had slipped down her arm, hopped to the floor, and padded off through the sea of folding chairs.

Chapter Three

Nibs! Fear swept through Maddy as she craned her head to see where the little cat had gone. She was so small – what if someone stepped on her in the crowded room? Luckily, no one seemed to notice that there was a cat no larger than a mouse prowling about – everyone was busy looking at the next item up for bid.

Rachel had seen her, though. "Where's she *going*?" she whispered in Maddy's ear.

"I don't know!" Maddy stood up, her pulse beating hard. "Um – I have to go to the loo," she said hastily to Aunt Tilly, edging past her.

"Me too!" Rachel jumped up as well, and the two girls squeezed their way down the row of seats. As soon as they reached the back of the room, Maddy dropped to her hands and knees, peering anxiously through the forest of chair legs and human legs. There was no sign of the little cat anywhere!

Rachel crouched down beside her. "Maybe she went into the other room," she suggested in a low voice.

Maddy glanced at the room where all the items were taken after bidding. There was an official-looking guard standing near the door, and she

swallowed. "Do you think we'd be allowed in?"

Rachel nudged her, grinning. "No, but it doesn't matter, Maddy. All you have to do is go shadowy, and you can sneak right past him!"

Of course! Maddy's heart leaped as she realized Rachel was right. Part of the cat magic was that each cat could give Maddy a special feline power. With Nibs, Maddy could go *shadowy*, which was almost like being invisible. Closing her eyes, Maddy took a deep breath and thought, *Cat . . . cat . . . cat!* Almost immediately she felt the familiar magic swirling through her, prickling and fizzing in her veins.

"Wow," gasped Rachel. "You know, I can never get used to that, no matter how often I see it. Or *don't* see it, rather!"

Opening her eyes, Maddy looked down at herself with satisfaction. Her physical form had faded right away until she looked like a barely visible ghost. Perfect!

"Be right back," she whispered to Rachel.

Her friend nodded, obviously not quite knowing where to look. "Good luck!"

Maddy made her way unseen towards the door. The guard was rather overweight, and Maddy sucked her breath in, making herself as thin as possible to slip past him. He stared off into the distance, not taking any notice of her.

Once inside, she saw tables piled high with purchased items, but no

sign of Nibs anywhere. Dropping to her hands and knees again, Maddy peered around the floor. "Nibs?" she whispered, as loudly as she dared. "Nibs, are you in here?" There was no reply. Oh, *where* had the tiny cat gone?

As Maddy got to her feet, she

noticed a queue at one end of the room, where people were paying for what they'd won. Her heart sank as she spotted the woman in the flowered top writing a cheque. And there was the cardboard box, right beside her! As Maddy watched, the woman picked up the box and carried it out of the back door.

"*Ouch!*" cried Maddy suddenly. Something small and sharp was jabbing its way up her jeans, like a tiny needle! Immediately she realized that it was Nibs, climbing back up to her pocket – but it was too late. Maddy's concentration had been shattered, and she flickered into view, just as Nibs's tiny black tail was disappearing into her jeans pocket.

The guard at the door started, and

stared at her in confusion. "Where did *you* come from?"

Maddy shrugged, and tried to smile. In her pocket, she could feel that Nibs had gone ceramic. "I just . . . walked in," she said truthfully.

"But – I could have sworn you weren't there a second ago . . ." The man trailed off, rubbing his hand across his eyes. "Never mind!" he said. "You need to leave; this room is for purchasers only."

Maddy left hastily, before he asked any more questions. She was dying to get Nibs on her own, and find out what she'd been up to – and ask her how on earth they were going to solve the problem now, with the locket gone.

But the little cat stubbornly stayed

ceramic for the rest of the afternoon. Long after they got back to Aunt Tilly's shop, Maddy hung around the upstairs bedroom, hoping that Nibs might come to life. Uneasily she thought that the cat's frozen expression looked rather secretive.

"Nibs, what *have* you been doing?" she whispered, touching the cat's cold nose.

But there was no response. Heaving a sigh, she slipped Nibs back in her

jeans pocket and headed downstairs, where Rachel was helping Aunt Tilly unpack the vintage clothing she'd bought.

"Isn't this gorgeous?" said Aunt Tilly proudly, holding up a long velvet jacket. It was a rich burgundy colour with a flared hem, like something a rock star might wear. "Now, I'll just give it a quick going over before I hang it up . . ." Humming to herself, Aunt Tilly inspected the jacket's lining, then checked the pockets. Her eyebrows flew up. "Why, what's this?"

Glancing up from a box of old shoes, Maddy stifled a gasp. Aunt Tilly was holding the golden locket!

"How strange! That wasn't mentioned in the item description," she said, checking the list that had

come with the clothes. "I'd better ring the auction house, and see if there's been some mistake."

As Aunt Tilly took out her mobile, Rachel hissed in Maddy's ear, "So *that's* what Nibs was doing – nicking the locket!"

Maddy nodded. No wonder Nibs had looked so furtive! Ducking

behind a cabinet as Aunt Tilly started to speak, Maddy took the little cat out of her pocket. “Nibs, come to life . . . *now*!” she ordered softly.

With a wavering ripple, cold ceramic melted into warm fur. From Maddy’s palm, Nibs blinked up at her with wide, innocent green eyes. “Yes?” she said.

“You stole the locket!” accused Maddy.

Nibs looked offended. “I did not. I merely appropriated it.”

“Appro— *what*?” spluttered Maddy.

“It means steal,” put in Rachel in a whisper.

Nibs gave her a cool look, the tip of her black tail twitching. “Look, you two, the woman who won the box only wanted the candlesticks. She was going to drop everything else off at a charity shop on her way home, I heard her say so. So where's the harm? We've got a problem that needs solving; the magic wouldn't have brought me to life otherwise!"

Maddy wavered. She knew perfectly well that it was wrong to take something that wasn't yours, but if the woman really had been planning to get rid of the locket anyway . . . "Well . . . maybe it's OK, then," she said.

Rachel still looked worried. "It doesn't matter if it's OK," she pointed out. "The auction house is sure to tell Aunt Tilly to bring the locket straight back!"

Just then, Aunt Tilly ended her

phone call. "Well, that's funny!" she exclaimed.

Nibs scampered up Maddy's arm to her shoulder, hiding behind her long brown hair. As Maddy turned round again, she saw Aunt Tilly examining the locket, looking bemused.

"They said they don't have a listing for it anywhere. It must have been in that pocket for ages, without anyone noticing!" She grinned at the girls. "How about that, eh? We've got a free Victorian locket! I wonder how much I can sell it for?"

CRASH!

All three of them jumped as a vase suddenly fell off a shelf, splintering into dozens of pieces on the floor.

Aunt Tilly blinked. "Why – how did *that* happen?" Going over to the

shelf, she stared at it in bewilderment. "Look, you can see from the dust marks that the vase wasn't even near the edge! It's like it just jumped off."

Rachel looked as confused as her aunt. "I don't know. Maybe a breeze caught it?"

Maddy felt the little cat stiffen on her shoulder. "Uh-oh," whispered Nibs.

"What?" murmured Maddy as Aunt Tilly started gathering up the broken pieces of china, and Rachel went to fetch the dustpan.

Nibs sighed, her whiskers tickling Maddy's earlobe. "I know what the problem is. Or at least, part of it. Oh dear, this is going to be tiresome!"

"Why?" whispered Maddy.

"You'll need to be shadowy to see,"

said Nibs grimly. "But trust me, this is *not* going to be fun."

Maddy opened her mouth to ask why again, but before she could, a cold shiver ran up her spine. She whirled round, staring at a corner of the shop. What was *that*? Her heart thudded as she looked into the empty corner.

She could have sworn she'd heard a dry, humourless chuckle . . . but no one was there.

Chapter Four

Maddy stared at the empty corner, her scalp prickling. Just then, the shop's bell jingled and a customer came in. As Aunt Tilly went to help her, Rachel sidled over to Maddy. "What's going on?" she whispered. "I could see you muttering to Nibs!"

"I don't know; she says I need to be shadowy to find out," said Maddy in an undertone. She glanced over to where Aunt Tilly was opening a glass case to show the woman an antique snuffbox.

"Go on, do it," hissed Rachel, reading Maddy's mind. "They won't notice."

"Yes, you might as well," said Nibs. She lashed her tail fretfully. "But don't be too surprised at what you see," she warned.

What did *that* mean? Feeling nervous, Maddy closed her eyes. *Cat*, she thought. *Cat . . . cat . . . cat!* As the magic tingled through her, she saw herself fade away to almost nothing.

On her shoulder, Nibs was now a dim outline of a cat, hardly visible either. "Over there, by the cabinet," she said in a weary voice. Taking a deep breath, Maddy turned to look.

"*Oh!*" she gasped, her hands flying up to her mouth. There was

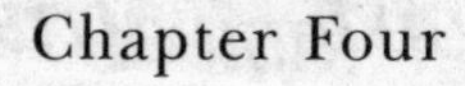

another woman standing beside Aunt Tilly and the customer! A very grumpy-looking woman, with grey hair pulled back in a bun, and an old-fashioned long black dress. She didn't seem very solid around the edges, and with a shudder, Maddy realized that she was looking at a ghost.

Nibs blew out a breath. "Honestly, how tiresome. I haven't had to deal with a ghost in years. And they make my fur go all clammy."

"What? What?" Rachel was whispering urgently.

"There's . . . a ghost in the shop," Maddy murmured back. As she spoke, the old woman turned to stare at them, and Maddy gulped.

Rachel blinked. "A *ghost*? But there's no such thing!"

The woman's eyes narrowed. "Um . . . tell *her* that," said Maddy weakly.

Her best friend blew out a breath. "Maddy, honestly! There must be another explanation. There's *no* scientific evidence for ghosts; they only exist in stories."

The ghost scowled at Rachel, her arms crossed over her thin chest. Maddy licked her lips. "Rache, can you be quiet, please? I think you're making her cross."

"Oh, this is ridiculous—" started Rachel.

Just then the customer spotted the

locket, lying on a nearby table. "How pretty!" she exclaimed, picking it up to examine it. "Is this for sale?"

"Yes, of course," said Aunt Tilly, going over to her. "It's genuine Victorian, and—"

"*Oh!*" screeched the woman suddenly. She dropped the locket as her hand flew to her head. "Someone just pulled my hair!"

Maddy winced. It had been the ghost, of course — she'd darted over the moment the woman had touched the locket, and now stood with her hands on her hips, as if daring her to touch the necklace again.

"But no one's there," said Aunt Tilly blankly. "Are you all right?"

The woman rubbed her head, looking around with a frightened

expression. "No, I – I think I'd better go," she stammered, taking a step back. "I . . . I don't feel very well." Gripping her handbag, she hurried out of the door.

As Aunt Tilly stared after the woman, Maddy quickly turned visible again. The ghost faded from view – which wasn't very comforting when Maddy knew she was still there somewhere, unseen!

"What an odd woman!" exclaimed Aunt Tilly after she'd gone. "Never mind – you win some, you lose some." Suddenly, she rubbed her arms. "Brr, it's got sort of chilly in here, hasn't it?"

"Chilly and *clammy*," muttered Nibs sourly in Maddy's ear. "Ghosts – ick."

"Um . . . I think Maddy and I are

going to go upstairs for a little while," said Rachel, shooting Maddy a look that said, *We need to talk!*

Aunt Tilly's eyebrows rose. "Don't you want to help me finish sorting these clothes?"

Maddy nodded hard. "In a bit," she said. "We just need to, er . . . do something first!" She was itching to get upstairs too. She knew Rachel must be dying to find out exactly what was going on . . . and so was she!

Up in the little bedroom, Nibs prowled back and forth on the dressing table. "Well, it's obvious that the ghost is attached to the locket in some way," she grumbled. "I've seen this kind of thing before, and believe me, it's never easy to solve."

"But there's no such *thing* as ghosts," protested Rachel for the tenth time.

Sitting down beside Maddy's hairbrush, Nibs rolled her eyes and didn't respond.

"So how do you explain the customer?" demanded Maddy. "And

the vase flying off the shelf?"

Rachel lifted her hands up. "I don't know! But there *must* be a better explanation than a – a spook, floating about!"

Maddy glanced around nervously, half afraid that the ghost had followed them upstairs and might be cross! But everything was silent. "Nibs, what's the problem that we need to solve?" she asked the cat. "Do we need to make the ghost go away again?"

Nibs's black fur gleamed as she gave a feline shrug. "I don't know exactly. We'll have to talk to the ghost tonight, and see what's going on. I have my *suspicions*, mind," she added with a disdainful sniff.

"What?" asked Maddy nervously, biting her thumb.

Nibs shook her head. "I won't say just yet. But I hope I'm wrong."

Rachel looked ready to explode. "I can't *believe* the two of you, sitting there talking about ghosts as if they really exist!"

Maddy felt like shaking her. "Rache, come on! You believe in magic, but not ghosts? That doesn't make much sense."

"That's . . . different," said Rachel

weakly. "Magic *does* exist; I've seen it with my own eyes."

"And I've seen the ghost with mine!" said Maddy, exasperated.

Tucking her paws under her, Nibs gazed at Rachel with unwavering green eyes. "Maddy's right, you know – you're not being very logical about this," she pointed out. "If you believe in me, then why not ghosts?"

Rachel bit her lip, looking cornered. Finally she burst out, "But I don't *want* there to be ghosts!"

"Be that as it may . . ." said Nibs dryly.

Rachel went pale. "So you mean there – there really *is* one, right here in the shop?" she asked in a tiny voice.

All at once Maddy remembered

that her friend had never liked scary stories very much, and refused to even look at horror films. A rush of sympathy swept over her. Rachel was *scared*!

"Don't worry," she said, trying to sound braver than she felt herself. "The ghost can't hurt us . . . or at least . . . not very much, hopefully . . ." She trailed off, remembering the woman's screech as the ghost had yanked her hair!

Obviously remembering the same thing, Rachel gave a small, frightened squeak. Padding to the edge of the dressing table, Nibs rubbed her tiny head against Rachel's arm. "Trust me, ghosts are overrated," she said. "The scariest thing about them is the way they make your fur go all icky. And

you don't even *have* fur, so you'll be fine!"

Rachel stroked Nibs's back, but she didn't look very comforted. "Do we – do we really have to go downstairs and talk to it tonight?"

"Well . . . *you* don't," said Maddy slowly. She knew that the problem was her responsibility, not Rachel's . . . but she really hoped that her friend would come with her. Even with Nibs along, Maddy didn't fancy going downstairs into the dark shop on her own, with a ghost there!

Rachel took a deep breath. "No, I'll – I'll come," she said. She gave a feeble smile. "It's scientific research, right? I've *got* to!"

"Thanks," said Maddy fervently. "You're the best friend in the whole world."

Nibs blinked up at them. "Well, now that that's settled, my chin seems to have a bit of an itch . . ."

With a grin, Maddy scratched the little cat's throat with her fingernail, and felt it almost vibrate as Nibs began to purr. "Ooh, very nice," she said happily, kneading her tiny paws against the dressing table. "You know, it's so good to be back that it's even worth dealing with a ghost!"

Once Aunt Tilly had fallen asleep that night, the two girls crept down the narrow flight of stairs. "I wish you didn't have to go shadowy," whispered Rachel, her voice quivering. "It'll be like being down there with *two* ghosts!"

"At least you don't have to talk to her," Maddy whispered back. Remembering the ghost's angry expression, she really wasn't looking forward to this very much.

At the bottom of the stairs was the door leading to the shop. Both girls hesitated, glancing at each other in the dim light. "Go on, open it," muttered Maddy.

Rachel looked alarmed. "No, you!"

"It's *your* aunt's shop," said Maddy quickly.

"Yes, but it's *your* ghost that you have to talk to!"

From Maddy's shoulder, Nibs let out an impatient breath. "Well, *I* can't open it," she pointed out, her tiny claws clutching at the material of Maddy's dressing gown. "So one of you has to!"

"Together," suggested Maddy, and Rachel nodded. They both put their hands on the doorknob. "One . . . two . . . three!" counted Maddy. And at the same time, the two girls opened the door.

Chapter Five

The shop lay in gloom before them. Maddy swallowed hard. Usually she loved Aunt Tilly's shop: it was so quirky and cluttered; but right now she'd give anything for it to be a bit more ordinary! A stuffed owl seemed to leer at her, and there were weird shadows everywhere.

With a quick bound away from Maddy's arm, Nibs leaped lightly onto the counter, where she sat beside an old-fashioned hotel bell larger than

she was. “Showing off, are we?” she grumbled, gazing upwards. Maddy felt her heart skip. What was Nibs looking at?

“Is – is the ghost here right now?” whimpered Rachel, pressing close against Maddy.

Nibs nodded. “You’d better go shadowy, Maddy. We need to get this sorted.”

Maddy gulped – though really, she supposed it *was* better to see the ghost than not see her. Otherwise it was like having a wasp in the room, and not knowing exactly where it was!

Drawing the magic to her, Maddy felt herself start to tingle. Rachel quickly grabbed her hand. "*Don't* let go," she said. "I want to know you're really there!"

"I won't," said Maddy, squeezing Rachel's fingers. *Cat,* she thought. *Cat . . . cat.* As she faded from view, she stifled a startled squawk. The ghost was right there, floating in the air above them! She seemed to glow in the faint light, and her black dress billowed slightly, as if caught in a breeze.

"Well, you took long enough," observed the ghost in a dry, scratchy voice. Her expression was dour.

"Erp," said Maddy weakly, staring upwards. Her eyes felt as if they might bulge right out of her head.

"Oh my gosh, I heard her!" moaned Rachel. "There – there really *are* ghosts!"

The ghost gave a chuckle that sounded like dry leaves rustling together. "Yes, I can sometimes make myself heard in the dead of night . . . to those who listen."

Nibs sat scowling. "Well, come down here so we can talk to you, then. You've got yourself into some bother, haven't you? And I've a feeling I know *how*, too," she added darkly.

Maddy stared as the ghost floated downwards until she was standing in the air right in front of them, her ghostly feet still a few centimetres off the floor. "A magical cat," she said, gazing at Nibs. "Oh, I know your type, all right!"

"Yes, I'm sure you do," said Nibs, sounding stern. "You were dabbling, weren't you? That's how you got into this mess!"

"*Dabbling?*" The ghost drew herself up, offended. "I did no such thing, cat! I, Josephine Moore, was a proper practitioner of the art."

"Ha," said Nibs flatly. "If you were anything other than a dabbler, you wouldn't be here now, tied to a locket."

"What are they talking about?" hissed Rachel in Maddy's ear as Josephine fell into a fuming silence.

But Maddy had a horrible feeling that she knew. "Do you mean *magic*?"

she burst out. "Like – witchcraft?"

"*Witchcraft?*" said Rachel. "But . . ." She trailed off. Maddy knew that she was yearning to say, *But there's no such thing!*

"Witchcraft, the dark arts – whatever you might call it," allowed Josephine, her wrinkled face turning crafty as she peered at Maddy. "You're one too, I suppose. This impertinent beast is your familiar, I take it?"

Maddy knew that a familiar was an animal that helped a witch with her spells. "Sort of," she hedged. It seemed easier to agree, rather than explaining what was really going on! "And, um . . . we really want to help you. There's a problem that needs solving, isn't there?"

Josephine heaved a sigh, her thin shoulders drooping. "There certainly is," she said. She pointed dramatically to the golden locket, which now rested inside the jewellery case – a free-standing wooden cabinet with shelves inside it, and a glass top and sides. "Do you see that locket? It was my own when I was alive, and through a series of circumstances that were *no fault of mine* . . ."

"Let me guess; you got the spell

wrong," finished Nibs, stifling a tiny feline yawn.

Josephine looked sulky as she floated in front of them. "I was only trying to protect it," she said. "It was my mother's, and I wanted to be sure it would always be worn by one of *my* female descendants too. But instead . . ."

"But instead you became tied to it," said the little cat.

"Yes," admitted Josephine heavily. "And now I can never rest until it goes to my great-granddaughter. It's rightfully hers now – her initials are the same as mine." Maddy stared as the ghost reached right into the glass cabinet. She pulled the locket out; there was a shimmer as it passed through the glass. "You see? JM," she said, pointing to the intricate swirls. "She *must* have it!"

"But that shouldn't be very hard," said Maddy in relief. "If her name is Josephine Moore too, all we have to do is find her!" Then she stopped, thinking. "Of course . . . it's probably a pretty common name." She frowned. In fact, the name reminded her of something, though she couldn't quite think what.

"No, it *will* be easy!" burst out Rachel. She seemed to have got over her initial fear as she eagerly straightened her glasses. "All we have to do is go onto a genealogy website!"

"A *what*?" asked Maddy. She saw that Josephine and Nibs looked confused as well.

"Genealogy," repeated Rachel. "You know, like family trees. My father's really into tracing our ancestors. He says all you need is the person's name and where they lived, and you can find out all sorts of things on the internet!"

Maddy started to say something, then stopped. Rachel sounded so excited that she hated to disagree with her . . . but somehow she had a feeling that the magic wouldn't have brought Nibs to life if the solution were as simple as looking on the internet.

"Is this some arcane magic?" asked

Josephine, narrowing her eyes.

"Close enough – she's talking about computers, I think," said Nibs dryly. She settled down on the counter, tucking her tiny paws under her.

"Yes, exactly," said Rachel. She peered around, obviously trying to work out where the ghost was to speak to her. "So, Mrs Moore, all we have to do is go onto one of these websites and put in your name and where you lived and all that. Then we'll be able to find your great-granddaughter, easy-peasy!"

The ghost looked uncomfortable. She crossed her arms, looking away. "Erm . . ."

"What is it?" said Nibs sharply.

"Well . . . I don't actually remember

where I lived," confessed the ghost.

Somehow, Maddy wasn't very surprised! "You don't?" she echoed weakly. "But—"

Josephine's black dress rustled around her as she bobbed in the air. "Being a ghost is difficult, you know – you forget things," she said in a grumpy voice.

"Wonderful," muttered Nibs, giving Maddy a meaningful look. "You see? I told you this sort of thing is never easy. *And* I can feel my fur going all clammy." She started washing herself pointedly.

It was, in fact, quite cold and uncomfortable-feeling in the shop, particularly standing so close to Josephine herself – though Maddy thought Nibs had been a bit tactless to mention it! The ghost scowled at the little cat.

Rachel appeared deep in thought. "Well – you probably lived round here, don't you think? I mean, how did your locket end up at the estate sale otherwise?"

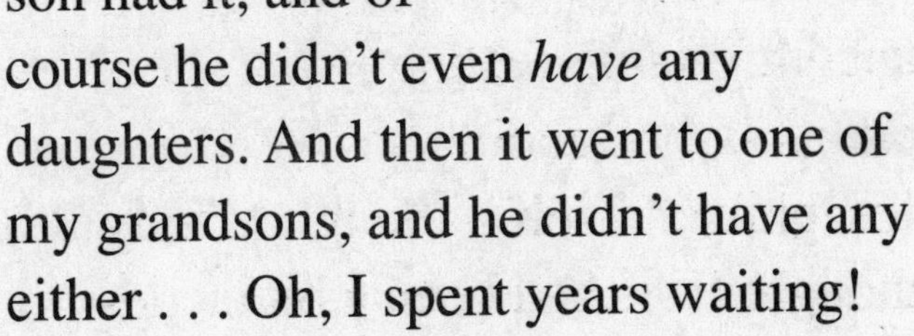

Josephine stamped her foot in the air. "I don't know, I tell you!" she said in frustration. "I spent years and years attached to the locket when my son had it, and of course he didn't even *have* any daughters. And then it went to one of my grandsons, and he didn't have any either . . . Oh, I spent years waiting!

And then after a while I seemed to just . . . go to sleep."

"To sleep?" echoed Maddy. Despite how prickly Josephine seemed, she found herself feeling sorry for the ghost. The long years of waiting sounded awful.

Josephine nodded her grey head. "All I know is that a few days ago, I woke up. And somehow I knew that I have a great-granddaughter now, and that the locket *must* go to her – it's my

last chance to truly rest."

"Where were you when you woke up?" asked Rachel, her eyes wide.

"In a dusty, untidy attic – whoever put my locket up there certainly didn't care much about keeping it safe!" Josephine shuddered. "Anyway, men were busy moving boxes, clearing the attic out. My locket was lying on the floor and I picked it up and put it in one of the boxes, so that it wouldn't be left behind. And now here I am!"

Maddy nodded slowly, thinking. "That must have been the house where the things at the auction came from," she said. "Rachel, couldn't we go there? They might know something about the locket!"

Rachel's face lit up. "Yes!" she exclaimed. "Aunt Tilly said it was the old Fletcher house – that's not very far from here at all. We'll ask if we can go tomorrow."

"Now *that's* what I call thinking, Maddy," said Nibs approvingly from the counter. Maddy felt a warm glow. Nibs didn't give praise very often – she must think it was a really good idea!

"Well, I hope you find my great-granddaughter quickly," said Josephine. "Because, I must say, I'm not best pleased to find my locket in a *shop*. Why, anyone could buy it! Though of course they won't," she added.

Rachel blinked. "Er . . . why not?"

"I'll stop them, of course," said Josephine in her scratchy voice. "You don't think I'll allow my locket to be sold, do you? It's staying right here until my great-granddaughter is found."

Maddy's throat went dry as she realized what Josephine meant. "You mean you'll pull someone's hair again, or knock things over, or—"

"Anything it takes!" confirmed Josephine with a cackle. Uneasily Maddy thought she sounded very much like a witch when she laughed like that! The ghost's voice faded as Josephine began to go dim. "So you'd better find my great-granddaughter quickly . . . or I doubt your aunt's shop will continue to receive much custom . . ." With an almost inaudible *pop*, Josephine vanished from view.

"But that's blackmail!" burst out Rachel, her face reddening. "You can't do that – and besides, we've already *said* that we'll help – we're really going to try!"

Maddy put her other hand on Rachel's arm. "Um, Rache . . . she's gone now." She made herself visible again, and the two girls stared at each other in the dim light.

Rachel rubbed her forehead. "I was just . . . arguing with a ghost," she said in a daze. Despite the seriousness of the situation, Maddy couldn't help smiling as they slipped up the stairs, with Nibs riding perched on her shoulder again.

"So does that mean you believe in them now?" she whispered as the girls got back to their bedroom. Distantly they could hear the sound of Aunt Tilly's snores.

Rachel made a face as she crawled into her bed. "It's sort of hard not to! We've *got* to find Josephine's great-granddaughter – she could really hurt Aunt Tilly's business otherwise! And Aunt Tilly needs all the customers she can get; I heard Mum say so."

"Oh, the ghost will definitely make trouble, all right," said Nibs. She prowled down to Maddy's elbow, where she sat lashing her tail grimly. "Ghosts always do."

"But don't worry, Rache," said Maddy quickly. "I'm sure our idea will work. We'll find her great-granddaughter in no time!" Then she fell silent, remembering that Nibs would have to leave once the problem was solved. Though Maddy didn't want anything to hurt Aunt Tilly's shop, she hated the idea of Nibs leaving soon. Swallowing hard, she tried to push the thought from her mind.

Nibs rubbed her sleek black fur against Maddy's thumb. "It'll all work out," she said gently. Maddy smiled as she stroked the tiny cat. Though it had been over a year now, she still couldn't get used to having such amazing magic in her life.

The three sat up talking for a while, keeping their voices low. Maddy told Rachel what the ghost had looked like, since she hadn't been able to see her. Rachel shook her head at the description of the grumpy elderly lady in black, with her grey hair in a bun. "You know, I think I actually would have guessed all that, even if you hadn't told me!" Turning on her side, she plumped up her pillow. "Anyway, I suppose we'd better get some sleep.

It's really late."

"Yes, dealing with ghosts always tires me out," said Nibs with a feline yawn.

To Maddy's delight, the little cat curled up on the pillow next to her to sleep. At home she always slept in Maddy's old doll's house – it was lovely having her right beside her! Maddy rested a finger on Nibs's side, feeling her sleek softness as the tiny cat slept.

Nibs is right, she thought, closing her eyes. *It'll all work out*. Somehow, they'd get the locket to Josephine's great-granddaughter.

But then, as Maddy was drifting off, an awful thought came into her mind. Would the people at the Fletcher house really want to help them? After all, they'd been the ones who sold the locket in the first place.

It might be that Josephine's great-granddaughter didn't even *want* the locket . . . and what on earth would they do then?

Chapter Six

The next morning Maddy wasn't surprised to find Nibs gone from her pillow. Thankfully, she'd remembered to leave the porthole window open a crack the night before. Glancing at it with a smile, she knew that the little cat had gone off hunting for her breakfast as usual.

"But we're on the first floor!" gasped Rachel, peering out of it. "What if she falls or something?"

"She'll be fine," said Maddy as she

got dressed. As if to prove her point, there was a slight rustle in the ivy, and Nibs's tiny form leaped up onto the curved sill.

"Good morning," she said, beginning to wash her face. "It *is* nice to be beside the sea. I've just had a lovely bit of fish. Delicious!"

"*Fish*?" Maddy felt her eyes widen. "Do you mean you caught one? But how did you – I mean—"

Nibs gazed blandly at her, not answering. Maddy held back a sigh. She knew perfectly well that none of the cats ever told her anything unless they wanted to – so she'd probably never find out how a cat the size of a mouse had managed to go fishing in the sea!

Looking a bit stunned, Rachel

shook her head as if to clear it. "Um . . . right. Well, should we go and ask Aunt Tilly about going to the Fletcher house today?"

As it turned out, there was a bus that left almost from Aunt Tilly's doorstep, which would take them right past the Fletcher house out in the countryside. "You're all right to go on your own, aren't you?" asked Aunt Tilly. "Easter is such a busy time for me – I can't really leave the shop."

"We'll be fine," Rachel assured her. "Aunt Tilly, could you take the locket out so that I can take a photo of it? We thought it'd be fun to research its history."

Aunt Tilly looked pleased. "What a good idea! If you find out anything, I could even do a little placard to

put beside it in the display case. Customers love that kind of thing!"

Maddy stiffened as an antique clock on a nearby table gave an ominous rattle. Luckily Aunt Tilly didn't seem to notice. Bending over the jewellery case, she drew out the locket, and Rachel took a few snaps of it with her phone. Just as she finished, a bright blue vehicle trundled past the front window.

"Oh, there's the bus!" Rachel quickly tucked the phone away into her handbag. "Come on, Maddy, we have to run!"

The girls just made the bus, sliding into a seat at the back, and a few minutes later they were trundling through the winding streets of Torton. Feeling Nibs come to life in her jeans pocket, Maddy furtively took her out. The little cat looked around with interest.

"What a strange way to travel, all crammed in together," she commented from her perch on Maddy's knee. "You wouldn't catch *cats* doing this."

Maddy grinned, imagining a bus

WARNING

load of cats. Beside her, Rachel was looking at the photos of the locket on her phone. "I'm glad that phones have cameras," she said. "Can you imagine if we'd had to bring the *locket* with us? We'd have Josephine on the bus as well!"

Soon the bus was out in the country. "There it is," said Rachel, ringing the bell that signalled to the driver to stop. "See – it's set back from the road a bit."

Peering out of the window, Maddy saw a large Georgian house at the end of a long drive. It looked a bit run down, though it obviously used to be very grand. As the girls hopped off the bus and started walking down the drive, Maddy felt her pulse quicken. What if she'd been right the night before, and no one here wanted the locket? The problem might *never* be solved!

But it turned out to be even worse than that. When the girls rang the bell and explained to the elderly woman who answered it why they were there, she frowned.

"I have no idea," she said, peering at the photo on Rachel's phone. "Are you sure it's from here?"

"Well . . . it was in a box of other things that came from here," said Maddy, her heart sinking.

"Hmm, how strange – I've certainly never seen it," said the woman. "Of course, I'm just loking after things at the moment. The Fletcher family haven't lived here in some time. They're about to sell the house now, so they've been clearing a lot of things out."

Rachel's eyes lit up. "So maybe *they* would know something about the locket!" she said. "Do you think you could give us their phone number?"

The woman shook her head. "I don't have it I'm afraid; I was employed through an agency. I'd love to help, but . . ." She shrugged, and handed the phone back. "Sorry, girls."

Discouraged, Maddy and Rachel trudged back down the drive. In her pocket, Maddy could feel that Nibs had turned ceramic again, and she touched the little cat's cool smoothness for comfort.

Suddenly she saw the FOR SALE

sign in the front garden. She hadn't paid much attention to it before, but now she stopped in her tracks as an idea came to her. "Rachel!" she cried. "What about the estate agents? *They* must have Mr Fletcher's phone number – maybe we can get it from them!"

"Brilliant!" said Rachel enthusiastically. She looked at the sign. "Vine and Wilson – there's one of those just a few shops away from Aunt Tilly's place, I'm sure of it. Come on, we'll get the bus back and go and see them right now!"

"Absolutely not," said the man.

Maddy and Rachel exchanged an agonized glance. They were in Vine and Wilson's office, sitting in a pair of uncomfortable office chairs. "But it's really important—" started Rachel.

"Little girl," interrupted the man behind the desk. He had thin brown hair combed over a bald patch, and a smile, Maddy thought, that was rather like a shark's. "Mr Fletcher is a very busy man. Do you really think he has time to answer frivolous questions about stray lockets?"

"But you could at least *ask* him!" burst out Maddy.

"I am sure that he would not thank me for doing so," said the estate agent haughtily. "Now, if you will excuse me, I have an appointment to keep." He stood up, giving the girls a pointed look. They had no choice but to get up as well, and start for the door.

With a quick scrabbling, Nibs came

to life in Maddy's pocket and bounded up her sleeve, ducking under her long hair. "Go shadowy as soon as you're out of sight!" she hissed in Maddy's ear. "Then you can double back and try to find the phone number!"

Maddy nodded, her heart pounding. The moment she and Rachel were away from the shop, she grabbed her friend's arm and ducked into an alley, quickly explaining the plan. "Go for it!" said Rachel, her eyes shining.

Drawing the cat magic to her, Maddy felt the familiar tingling as she faded from view. She wasn't a moment too soon. When she opened her eyes again, she saw the estate agent go striding past, holding a briefcase.

"I'll be back as soon as I can!" she cried to Rachel, and darted back to Vine and Wilson's office. Through the window she could see the other agent talking on the phone. As quietly as she could, she edged open the door and slipped invisibly inside.

"May I help—" the woman began, looking up.

She broke off, staring around the empty office in confusion. Maddy froze, suddenly feeling very visible! Finally the woman shrugged and went back to her phone call. "Never mind – I must be imagining things . . ."

Maddy let out a sigh of relief. "Come on," Nibs whispered from her shoulder. "Let's see what we can find out!"

Tiptoeing across to the empty desk, Maddy glanced over her shoulder. The estate agent was staring at her computer screen, not paying attention. Quickly Maddy opened an address book that was lying on the desk, and flipped through it. But when she came to F, there was no entry for Fletcher.

"Try the files!" hissed Nibs.

Maddy shook her head. The filing

cabinets lined one wall – there was no way she could start rifling through them and not be seen! Then she saw that the computer on the desk was still on. Could she find Mr Fletcher's email address, and contact him that way?

She bit her lip. Somehow, computers and magic didn't really seem to go together. She had a feeling that even if she *did* find an email address, it wasn't going to be much help. But she shook the thought away. It wasn't as if she had much choice!

She slid into the chair and quietly clicked the mouse, opening up the email browser. There were hundreds of emails! She scrolled down, feverishly looking for an address with 'Fletcher' in it. None appeared. This was like trying to find a needle in a haystack!

The shadowy Nibs was standing on the keyboard, staring upwards at the screen. "What's *that*?" she demanded softly, stretching up and pointing with her paw. Maddy saw that she was looking at the address book icon.

"Nibs, you're a genius!" she murmured. As she clicked on it, all the email addresses stored on the computer appeared in a neat table. Maddy moved the mouse down. Emerson . . . Fitzgerald . . . *Fletcher!* There it was!

Too late she remembered that she didn't have a pencil and paper with her. She stared intently at the address, trying to memorize it. Suddenly she jumped as she heard movement

behind her.

"Excuse me," said the agent on the phone. "Something odd is going on with the other computer – the screen keeps changing round, all by itself!"

Before Maddy could move, the woman had come over to the desk. Maddy snatched her hand away from the mouse just as the agent reached for it to close the address book. "Strange," she murmured, gazing at the screen – and then, to Maddy's horror, she sat down in the chair!

"ARGH!" they both shrieked at the same time. The woman jumped as if the chair was on fire.

"Who's there? *Who*?" she screeched, her eyes wide.

Maddy didn't answer; she was too busy leaping up from the chair and sprinting for the door. As she wrenched it open, she risked a glance over her shoulder and saw the woman gaping in shock at the door, apparently opening and closing on its own. Holding back a wild giggle, Maddy dashed into the alley, pleased that she'd managed to stay invisible despite the shock of being sat on. Her magical skills were growing stronger!

"Did you get it?" demanded Rachel as Maddy turned visible again beside her.

"I – I'm not sure," said Maddy, her pleasure fading. To her dismay, the email address seemed to have gone right out of her mind.

Nibs, who had bounded back onto Maddy's shoulder as she leaped off the chair, cleared her throat. "JWFletcher@

Fletcherenterprisesdotcodotuk," she said smugly, curling her tail about her legs.

"Hurrah!" exclaimed Maddy. She scooped the little cat up in her hand for a cuddle.

Rachel's eyes gleamed from behind her glasses. "Nibs, that's brilliant. We'll go back to Aunt Tilly's and write the email right now – and with any luck, we won't have a ghost around for much longer!"

Chapter Seven

When the girls returned to the shop, they found Aunt Tilly talking to a woman with long blonde hair and a flowing purple top. "My dear, you simply *must*," the woman was saying earnestly. "Who knows how it might end up otherwise?"

Aunt Tilly looked relieved to see the girls back – though Maddy had a feeling that this was because she was tired of talking to the woman on her own! "This is Clarissa, my new neighbour," she said as she introduced them. "She owns Magical Mysteries across the road."

The girls said hello. Maddy looked at Clarissa curiously, remembering the shop with the crystal ball in its window. So this was Aunt Tilly's new neighbour – the woman who was supposed to be psychic.

"Your Aunt Tilly says that she's been having *incidents* this morning," said Clarissa, her voice heavy with meaning. She wore a crystal pendant and a pair of long, dangling earrings.

"Incidents?" echoed Maddy. She and Rachel glanced at each other, the same thought reflected in both their faces: *Josephine!*

Aunt Tilly nodded, looking worried. "Yes, a few more things have fallen

off shelves. I really don't know what's going on – maybe we're having mini earthquakes or something."

"*And* don't forget that you said a man had his arm pinched by *invisible fingers*," added Clarissa. "Tilly, believe me – these are ghostly happenings, not earthquakes!"

Aunt Tilly rolled her eyes. "Don't be silly – there's no such thing as a ghost. He only *thought* he was pinched – he was probably just stung by a wasp."

Maddy managed not to laugh as she and Rachel glanced at each other. Aunt Tilly sounded exactly like Rachel had!

"Really, Tilly, you should leave this sort of thing to the experts," chided Clarissa. "Trust me, you have a ghost here, and if you don't do something about it, it could turn into a real problem."

"And what do you suggest I do?" asked Aunt Tilly dryly.

Clarissa drew herself up, earrings swaying. "As your friend and neighbour, I insist on holding a séance here, to get to the bottom of this!"

"A *séance*?" spluttered Aunt Tilly. "Clarissa, you must be mad!"

"I won't take no for an answer. At eight o'clock tonight we'll contact your ghost and move it to the other side, so that it will bother you no more. Trust me, Tilly, you'll thank me later." And with that, Clarissa swept out of the shop.

"What's a séance?" asked Rachel once she was gone. "Is it when you contact a ghost?"

"Yes, that's right," groaned Aunt Tilly. "Oh, well, I suppose I'll let her

do it – it'll be good for a giggle if nothing else, eh, girls?"

Maddy thought that Aunt Tilly looked as if she could use a laugh, just then! "Were they very expensive things that broke?" she asked sympathetically, leaning against one of the display tables.

Aunt Tilly nodded. "Unfortunately, yes – though I'm more worried about losing customers. Four different people left because of it."

"Were they, um . . . looking at the jewellery when it happened?" asked Rachel, biting her finger.

Aunt Tilly's eyebrows rose. "Yes, I think so, now that you mention it." She laughed. "Why? Do you girls think the new locket is haunted?"

Maddy felt her face redden.

"Well . . ."

"You can't be serious!" hooted Aunt Tilly. "No, it's just a funny coincidence – but I wish I could work out what's going on. I can't afford to keep losing customers." She let out a sigh. "Never mind. Who knows, maybe by some miracle Clarissa will be able to help!"

Maddy and Rachel spent a long time composing their email to Mr Fletcher, explaining that the locket had come from his estate, and that they were interested in finding out its history. Rachel attached the photos of the locket to the email.

"There!" she said, hitting *Send*. "Now all we have to do is wait." Her expression became anxious as she glanced back at the shop. "Let's hope he writes back really quickly."

Maddy felt torn. She didn't want Aunt Tilly to keep losing customers, but she didn't want Nibs to leave just yet, either. She nodded silently, stroking the little cat's cool ceramic body in her pocket.

Rachel seemed to realize what she was thinking, and shot Maddy an apologetic glance. "Sorry! I didn't

mean . . ."

"No, I know," said Maddy with a sigh. "And we *do* have to solve the problem." Pushing the thought away, she glanced at the clock. The séance was in just a few hours. Despite herself, she felt an excited tingle at the thought of it. "Do you think Clarissa really *has* got psychic powers?" she asked.

Rachel looked thoughtful as she turned off the computer. "Well, a few days ago I would have said definitely not – but now, who knows!" She sighed. "If Clarissa *can* communicate with Josephine, I hope that Aunt Tilly will listen to her. She doesn't believe in ghosts any more than I did!"

When Clarissa arrived that night,

they all sat down at a round table in the middle of the shop. Maddy was between Rachel and Aunt Tilly, with Nibs sitting crouched on her shoulder. "Now, we must all join hands," announced Clarissa. She was wearing a long, flowing dress and lots of jangling bracelets. "We need an unbroken circle of energy!"

Taking Rachel and Aunt Tilly's hands, Maddy glanced around, wondering where Josephine was. What would the ghost think of all this?

"Are the spirits there . . . ? Talk to me, spirits, talk to me . . ." intoned Clarissa, her eyes closed.

Nibs let out a disdainful sniff. "I doubt any spirits will be able to, this early in the evening," she murmured

in Maddy's ear. "Ghosts can normally only talk in the dead of night, when the world is still. A proper clairvoyant would know that!"

"Come to me . . . let me see you . . ."

Nibs gave a feline snigger. "Josephine's just appeared, right in front of her. If Clarissa could *really* see ghosts, she'd find her pretty hard to miss!"

Maddy gulped, staring at the air around Clarissa. The thought of Josephine standing right there was a bit creepy!

"Ah, I see . . . yes, yes . . ." murmured Clarissa, swaying slightly in her chair. "There are *two* ghosts here, not just one!"

"What?" cried Maddy before she

could stop herself. “But—”

Opening one eye, Clarissa shot Maddy a stern look. “You must keep quiet, or you will disrupt the energy.”

“Um . . . sorry,” said Maddy.

Clarissa closed her eyes again. “Two ghosts,” she continued. “One . . . one is that of a petulant young boy. He’s standing in the corner, watching us!”

Aunt Tilly glanced at the shadowy corner, looking slightly alarmed.

“Oh no, there’s not,” muttered Nibs. “And you should see Josephine’s face,” she added with a chuckle. “She looks ready to burst!”

Maddy winced, dreading what the ghost might do.

“And the other ghost . . . the other is a woman . . .”

Maddy's eyes widened as her heart skipped a beat in surprise. Had Clarissa seen Josephine after all?

But Clarissa went on: "She is very young, and very beautiful . . . She's dressed all in white . . ."

Rachel made a strange, strangled noise, and Maddy knew that she was trying not to burst out laughing. Imagining elderly, grumpy Josephine in her pitch-black dress, Maddy was having a hard time not laughing herself!

"Is she here for the locket?" asked Aunt Tilly, giving Rachel a warning look. "The girls think that the new locket might have something to do with it – you remember, I told you how I found it."

"Let me ask," said Clarissa.

Silence fell.

"What a phoney," hissed Nibs cheerfully, her whiskers tickling Maddy's ear. "She's not doing a thing but just sitting there!"

Finally Clarissa spoke again. "Yes, it is indeed the locket that she's here for," she said. "She wore it on her wedding day . . . and then she died on the way to her own wedding . . . Oh, what a tragedy . . . she can never rest now, until— *OW*!"

Clarissa broke off. "Someone pulled my hair!" she burst out, looking around accusingly.

"Well, it wasn't any of us," said Aunt Tilly, sounding taken aback. "We're all holding hands, remember?"

Clarissa went pale. "Er . . . yes," she said, with a nervous glance around her. "All right, um . . . shall I continue?" Clearing her throat, she started again, though Maddy thought she sounded much less sure of herself now!

"The bride was called . . . er . . . Sophia. She is here now, and she says she's haunting your shop because—"

"Uh-oh, that's done it," muttered Nibs, hunkering down on Maddy's shoulder. "Look out!"

Even though she was expecting it, Maddy couldn't hold back a shriek as the shop erupted into mayhem. The jewellery case rattled back and forth; coat sleeves flapped up and down on their racks; a champagne glass smashed onto the floor. Maddy gaped. Josephine must be flying about like a whirlwind! On the wall, the hands of an antique clock went spinning round and round, with a cuckoo popping out to chirp the time.

Everyone was staring, open-mouthed. Aunt Tilly gave an uncertain laugh. "Clarissa, you're pulling our legs, aren't you? *How* are you doing this?"

Clarissa gulped, her eyes wide. "Er – I – Sophia says that—"

THUMP! THUMP!

With a squeak, Maddy ducked as antique books started flying out from their shelves, all of them aimed at Clarissa! Fortunately Josephine didn't seem to be a very good shot.

As one of the books whizzed past Clarissa's head, the medium gave a stifled scream, her bracelets rattling. She looked wildly around. "Perhaps – perhaps we should draw the séance to a close now," she gasped. "I sense that the spirits are too restless to communicate with tonight!"

Aunt Tilly looked shaken. "Yes, I suppose that's for the best," she said, staring at the books on the floor. "Do you think there could really be a—" She stopped short. "No, there couldn't be!"

But Clarissa had already departed. In fact, Maddy thought, she'd practically run out of the door!

Rachel nudged Maddy with a grin. "I don't think she was expecting that!" she whispered. "Gosh, did you see how fast she went?"

Aunt Tilly blew out a breath and ran a hand through her short red hair. "Well, I just hope she doesn't go round telling people that my shop is haunted. I'm losing enough business as it is!" She frowned as she put the books back in place and picked up the broken glass. "But how on earth did . . ." She trailed off, shaking her head. "Never mind! It *must* have been Clarissa doing it all, somehow. And I don't appreciate it, I must say!"

Turning out the lights, Aunt Tilly

started for the stairs. "Come on, girls – I think it's time for bed."

"Wow," murmured Maddy to Rachel as they went up the stairs. "She's even more scientific than *you* are."

"I told you," Rachel whispered back. "There's just no way that Aunt Tilly would ever believe in a ghost – ever!"

Tap. Tap, tap. Maddy stirred drowsily at the feel of a tiny paw tapping her cheek. "Hey. Are you awake?" said a voice. Maddy's eyes fluttered open.

"Nibs!" she exclaimed softly. The little cat was sitting on her pillow, her green eyes gleaming in the moonlight. "We need to go and talk to Josephine," she said, staring up

at Maddy. "I can feel that she's very restless down there."

Maddy gulped. "Um . . . shall I wake Rachel?" She glanced at her friend, cosily asleep in the next bed.

But Nibs shook her head. "The fewer people, the better. I don't think Josephine's very happy with the living right now!"

"Oh, great," said Maddy weakly.

What if Josephine started throwing things at *her*? But she knew that this was part of having the magic in her life – sometimes she had to do things that she really didn't want to do.

Climbing quietly out of bed, Maddy pulled on her dressing gown. Nibs bounded up her arm, settling near her ear, and Maddy reached up and stroked her. The sleek little cat's warmth felt reassuring.

"OK," she whispered, squaring her shoulders. "I'm ready!"

The shop lay draped in shadows as Maddy creaked open the door. Taking a deep breath, she made herself go shadowy. As the tickling sensation ran through her, she opened her eyes again and saw Josephine, floating

back and forth across the shop as if she were pacing. The ghost's face was set in a scowl, and her black dress billowed around her.

She saw Maddy and stopped in mid-air. "*Who* was that idiotic woman?" she demanded in her scratchy voice.

Maddy swallowed hard. "Erm . . . she has a shop across the street."

"I've never been so insulted in my life – or in my death either, come to that!" fumed Josephine. "*A woman in*

white, a *petulant young boy* – what utter rubbish! She has *no* appreciation of the dark arts – none!"

"No, probably not," admitted Maddy. "But I think you scared her pretty badly. I doubt she'll ever try to hold a séance again!"

Nibs hopped down to the counter with a tiny *thump*. "Yes, you really must try to control yourself," she said sternly, lashing her slim tail. "Throwing tantrums won't help to find your great-granddaughter, you know. What if Aunt Tilly decides to get rid of the locket because it's too much trouble? The girls won't be able to help you at all then!"

Josephine went a bit more transparent, her thin shoulders drooping. "Oh, you're right, cat . . . my temper was always my downfall." Drifting over to the jewellery case, she gazed sadly down at her locket. "I do yearn to be free," she murmured. "It's been so many long years of being entrapped . . ." She turned to Maddy, her wrinkled face pleading. "Did you find anything out?"

Maddy hesitated. Suddenly Josephine looked very old and tired. She wished with all her heart that she could tell her that yes, they had found her great-granddaughter and everything was OK.

"Well . . . not yet," she said. "But Rachel and I have sent an email to the owner of the house, and – and hopefully we'll hear something soon." The ghost blinked, and Maddy could see that she didn't understand. "Email," she repeated. "It's like a letter, only faster."

"We shall wait and see, then," said Josephine. "But I have a feeling . . ." She sighed, wavering in the air.

"What?" asked Maddy with a prickle of alarm.

"That nothing will come of it – that my great-granddaughter will never be found," said the ghost heavily. "I fear that I'm doomed to be tied to this locket for ever!"

Chapter Eight

As the days passed with no response from Mr Fletcher, Maddy started to worry that Josephine was right. Meanwhile, things weren't going very well in the shop, either. Whenever anyone looked at the locket in the display case, Josephine scared them away – by pulling their hair, or pinching them, or knocking things over with a *bang*. Aunt Tilly had started to become very jumpy, almost wincing whenever anyone asked to see the locket.

"I don't know, girls," she sighed on Friday afternoon. "Maybe there *is* something strange about this locket." She was standing at the counter, turning the golden locket over in her hand. "I just don't know how else to explain all the things that are happening!"

Maddy hesitated, wondering if they should tell Aunt Tilly the truth. Rachel caught her eye and shook her head. *She wouldn't believe you!* she mouthed.

Rachel seemed to be right. A moment later, Aunt Tilly blew out a breath, looking irritated with herself. "Oh, what am I saying – it's just a locket!" She shoved it roughly back into the display case. It came to rest near the edge of a glass shelf, winking in the light.

Straightening up, Aunt Tilly said, "Tell you what, why don't you girls do me a favour?" She picked up a stack of Tilly's Treasures flyers from the counter. "Go down to the beach and hand these out to people – let's get some more customers in here!"

The girls were happy to oblige, and soon they were strolling beside the sea, their shoes leaving tracks in the damp sand. Maddy breathed deeply. The sea air smelled wonderful – so fresh and salty!

"I'm taking my shoes off," said Rachel, unbuckling her sandals.

Maddy did too, giggling at the wet sand squelching between her toes. Feeling Nibs come to life in her pocket, she grinned and took the little cat out. Glancing around, she put her on the sand and Nibs went bounding off, leaving tiny pawprints behind her. "Watch me catch a wave!" she yowled.

The two girls almost cried with laughter to see Nibs stalking the water, and then scampering away again when it licked too close to her black paws. Finally Maddy spotted a woman heading towards them, and quickly picked Nibs up again. She scrambled away into Maddy's pocket.

The woman stared at Maddy as she drew close. "Did you bring your *hamster* to the beach?" she asked.

Maddy barely managed not to laugh. In her pocket she could feel Nibs bristling at being called a hamster! "Um, yes . . . she really loves it!" said Maddy. Hastily she offered the woman a flyer. "Here – try Tilly's Treasures!"

Rachel had covered her mouth with her hands; she burst out giggling as the woman went off. "Oh, Maddy, that was brilliant! Come on – let's get an ice cream."

With the sun hot on their heads, the two girls headed over to the ice-cream van and got a pair of ninety-nines.

Sitting on a bench to eat them, Maddy placed Nibs on her shoulder, so that the little cat could lick bits of the treat too.

"Not bad," said Nibs thoughtfully. She had dabs of vanilla ice cream all around her mouth. "For human food, not bad at all!" She took another lick with her tiny tongue.

Chapter Eight

Rachel leaned her head back as she ate her chocolate flake. "Isn't this brilliant? I wish we could live beside the beach all the time."

Burrowing her toes into the sand as she licked her ice cream, Maddy agreed wholeheartedly. But as the afternoon wore on, she began to feel worried. Time was passing. Their stay at Aunt Tilly's was nearly over, and they still hadn't solved the problem.

"Come on, we'd better go back to your aunt's and check the email again," she said to Rachel finally, sticking the remaining flyers in her bag. "Mum will be coming to take us home tomorrow afternoon – we *have* to sort the problem out by then!"

Heading back to the antique shop, the

two girls went into Aunt Tilly's tiny office and switched on the computer. Glancing over her shoulder to make sure Aunt Tilly wasn't watching, Maddy took Nibs out of her pocket and placed her on the desk calendar. The little cat shivered into life again, no larger than one of the dates on the calendar page.

"Any news?" asked Nibs, flicking her slim black tail. She sounded her usual brisk self once more, but there was still a tiny dab of ice cream on her face! Maddy smiled at her affectionately, running her finger down the cat's sleek back.

"We've got an email!" burst out Rachel from the computer.

Maddy rushed across to look. Nibs bounded over as well, leaping up onto

the keyboard. Eagerly Rachel opened the email and started to read. "*Dear Maddy and Rachel, Thank you for your email. I've looked at the photos you sent, and I'm afraid there's been some mistake*— Oh, no!" Rachel broke off.

Maddy kept reading, the words tumbling together in her disappointment: "*The locket isn't one I've seen before, and Moore is not a family name. So I'm afraid I can't help you, but do wish you luck in your search. Yours sincerely, Matthew Fletcher.*" She sank down onto the desk, staring at the screen. She'd been right – the email hadn't been any use at all. What *now*?

"Ah," said Nibs, sitting on the *shift* key and worriedly twitching her whiskers. "Well, that's unfortunate."

"Oh, what *now*?" groaned Rachel, flopping back in the chair. "There must be thousands of Josephine Moores in the country! How are we ever going to find the right one?"

Maddy shook her head, her spirits sinking. "I don't know. We don't even know where to begin looking – it'll take ages."

Nibs leaped onto Maddy's arm. "You know, I don't think we're going about this the right way," she said briskly. She paced up and down Maddy's shirt sleeve, her tiny paws padding on the material. "Maddy, think! Why would the magic come to you? Why should *you* be the one to solve this problem?"

"What do you mean?" asked Rachel, adjusting her glasses.

The little cat sat on Maddy's elbow; Maddy could feel her slight, furry weight. "I mean that the answer might lie with with Maddy herself," she said. "It makes a lot more sense than having to check out thousands of Josephine Moores!"

Maddy bit her lip in bewilderment. "Me? But I don't know anyone called Josephine Moore . . ." She trailed off as, once again, she had the strange sense that she *had* heard that name before – or maybe not exactly, but one very similar to it.

"What?" said Rachel, seeing the expression on Maddy's face.

Maddy started to shake her head – and then it came to her. "Oh!" she cried. "I don't know anyone called Josephine Moore, but I know a *Jodie* Moore – she used to live in our neighbourhood!"

"JM!" shouted Rachel, bouncing on the chair. "Oh, Maddy, that could be it – because Josephine didn't say that the J stood for her *own* name, did she? She just said that her great-granddaughter had the same initials as she did!"

"Where's this Jodie Moore now?" asked Nibs, her black face intent.

Maddy shook her head. "I don't know – she and her family moved away years ago. I was only little, and she was five or six years older than me – we didn't keep in touch or anything."

"Let's see if she has a Facebook page," said Rachel, spinning the chair back towards the computer. A few minutes later, a page for Jodie Moore came up. Maddy blinked to see the teenager's photo on the screen. It was Jodie, all right – but she looked so grown up now!

"*Torton!*" screeched Rachel, looking at the "location" information. "Oh, Maddy, she's right here! This has to be it!"

Maddy's heart leaped as she saw the word *Torton* on the screen. Jodie

was here! Maybe she really *was* the right JM.

"Let's send her a message, and ask if she had a great-grandmother called Josephine Moore," said Rachel eagerly, reaching for the keyboard.

"No," said Maddy suddenly. "I don't think computers are the way to solve this, Rache – the magic wouldn't have come to me otherwise.

We have to go and talk to her in person!"

Nibs padded down Maddy's arm to sit on her palm. "I agree," she said briskly. "If she's here in Torton, then let's go and find her. There's no time to lose!"

Rachel hesitated, then nodded and turned off the computer. "OK, you're probably right. Come on, we'll ask Aunt Tilly where the Moores live. She knows everyone round here!"

The Moores' house was only a few streets away, on a small, twisting lane. The girls went first thing the next morning, following Aunt Tilly's directions carefully. "Let's see, she said it had a red door," muttered Rachel, peering at the houses as they passed.

Suddenly Maddy clutched Rachel's arm. "I think that's her!" she gasped.

Two teenage girls were coming along the street, talking and laughing. One of them, Maddy was sure, was Jodie – she had the same long dark hair and bright, friendly face as in the photo. Maddy smiled hopefully at Jodie as the two girls passed them, but Jodie obviously didn't recognize her – she and her friend walked by without even giving Maddy and Rachel a second glance.

Once they were out of earshot, Rachel shoved her lightly. "Maddy, you numpty! Why didn't you say anything to her? Come on, let's catch them up."

Maddy shook her head, realizing

how impossible this was. "Rachel, she didn't even know who I was! I can't just go up to her and say that she used to live in my neighbourhood years ago, and does she have a great-grandmother called Josephine – she'd think I was mad!"

Rachel frowned. "Hmm. You might be right," she admitted.

"We've just got to get her into the shop somehow," said Maddy. "If it *is* her, then I bet Josephine will know, and we can see that she gets the locket!"

"How, though?" said Rachel, looking worried. "I think the locket's sort of expensive – what if Jodie doesn't have enough money for it? We can't just *give* it to Jodie, when Aunt Tilly thinks it belongs to *her*."

Maddy shook her head. "I don't know – let's just get her into the shop for now."

Rachel stared at her. "Yes, good plan. But, Maddy, *how* exactly are we going to do that?"

Maddy bit her lip, realizing that she had absolutely no idea how to get Jodie into Tilly's Treasures. Worry gripped her. Their plan *had* to work; she and Rachel would be gone in a few hours! In her pocket, she felt Nibs shimmer into life. A moment later, the tiny cat had bounded up to Maddy's shoulder.

"Leave it to me," she hissed, her whiskers tickling Maddy's ear. "I'll run on ahead and see what they're talking about – maybe it's something we can use!"

Before Maddy could respond, Nibs had scrambled down Maddy's jeans to the ground and bounded off down the pavement after the two teenage girls, turning shadowy as she went.

"Wow, she doesn't waste any time," said Rachel.

Maddy stared down at the pavement. "We'd better stop walking – what if she comes back while she's still shadowy, and we don't see her? We could tread on her!"

The two girls waited fretfully for several minutes. Finally Maddy felt something tugging on her shoelace, and there was Nibs, becoming visible again as she watched. "What did you stop walking for?" asked the little cat in surprise, peering up at her. "I had to run all the way back!"

Maddy grinned as she scooped the cat up in her hands. "We were worried we might not see you, and hurt you or something," she explained, stroking Nibs's sleek black fur.

Nibs rolled her green eyes. "As if I couldn't take any better care of myself than that!" she chided affectionately, rubbing her head against Maddy's fingers. "Anyway, we're in luck – Jodie is going to a party tonight, and she wants to get something really unusual to wear. Tilly's Treasures would be just the place for her!"

"I've still got some flyers in my bag!" gasped Maddy. "Rachel, wait here – I'll be right back!" Pounding off in the direction Jodie and her friend had taken, Maddy soon spotted them heading into Torton's small town centre.

Racing to catch up with the two girls, Maddy skipped around in front of them. “Hi, um – I couldn’t help overhearing you before,” she said breathlessly. “And you know, if you’re looking for something unusual to wear, you *really* couldn’t do better

than Tilly's Treasures!" She offered the girls a flyer.

Jodie and her friend looked taken aback, but accepted the flyer. "Oh – this is that funny shop near the estate agent's, isn't it?" said Jodie, peering down at it.

Maddy nodded vigorously. "It's got *loads* of vintage clothes! Really unusual things that no one else will be wearing. And – and antique jewellery, and all sorts." She held her breath.

Jodie's friend, a blonde girl with perfect make-up, rolled her eyes. "Oh, come on – we don't want to go there, do we? Let's just go to Topshop."

"No, let's check it out," said Jodie, still gazing down at the brightly coloured flyer. "It'll just take a minute. Who knows, it might have just the thing!" She glanced up at Maddy with a smile. "Thanks!" she said.

Maddy smiled back as the two girls started off towards Aunt Tilly's shop. *Yes!* She'd done it! She gave a quick excited spin. Suddenly Nibs leaped up onto her shoulder, swishing her tail.

"Hurry!" hissed the little cat. "We have to get back to the shop before they do!"

Chapter Nine

Maddy dashed back to where Rachel was, and a minute later the two friends were sprinting through the cobbled streets. "Come on, I know a shortcut!" cried Rachel, pulling at Maddy's arm as she ducked down a side street.

In no time at all they arrived panting at the shop. Aunt Tilly was at the door, locking it. She looked at them in surprise. "Oh, there you are," she said. "I was just about to close up for a few minutes, and pop out to the post office."

"No!" cried Rachel. "I mean – I mean, Maddy and I will watch the shop for you, won't we, Maddy?"

Maddy nodded hard. "Yes, we'd love to!" She looked anxiously over her shoulder. Jodie and her friend might arrive at any moment!

Aunt Tilly's eyebrows rose. "Well, all right – if any customers come in, just tell them I'll be back in a minute." Then she sighed. "Not that it's likely I'll be seeing any customers, the way things have been going!"

As soon as Aunt Tilly was gone, Maddy said, "Right, I'd better turn shadowy, so that I can see Josephine."

Rachel nodded. "And I'll make sure that Jodie and her friend see the locket, when they get here!"

As Maddy faded from sight, she felt Nibs come to life again, climbing invisibly onto her shoulder. Josephine was floating near the ceiling, with her arms crossed over her stomach and her eyes closed. "Josephine, we think your great-granddaughter's on her way here!" hissed Maddy.

Josephine didn't respond. Her chest gently rose and fell, and a soft snore came from her lips. Maddy gaped. The ghost was *asleep*!

"Oh, great," muttered Nibs crossly, swishing her tail. "It can take them hours to wake up when this happens!"

"Josephine, you have to wake up!" cried Maddy. Jumping up, she tried to bat at the ghost with her hand, but Josephine was floating too high for her to reach. "You have to tell us whether this is your great-granddaughter—"

Maddy broke off as the shop door tinkled. Rachel, who looked like she'd been about to ask what was going on, snapped her mouth shut too. Jodie and her friend came wandering in. "Funny old place, isn't it?" said Jodie's friend, making a face. "Only *you* would go shopping for a party in here!"

But Jodie's eyes had lit up. "This is great!" she exclaimed, heading over to the rack of vintage clothes. "Look at all this stuff, Katie – *nobody* will be wearing anything like this tonight." She held up an old-fashioned shirt with a high collar.

"No, of course not – it's been out of fashion for about a hundred years!" giggled Katie. But she went over and joined Jodie at the rack, examining the clothes.

Up above, Josephine let out a blubbery snore that no one but Maddy seemed to hear.

Rachel slipped behind the counter. "Can I help you?" she said, adjusting her glasses. "I'm minding the shop while my aunt's gone."

The girls barely gave her a look. "We're OK, thanks," said Jodie, pulling out a green flapper dress with swinging beads. "Ooh, Katie, look at this!"

Katie shook her head with a grin. "You have *got* to be kidding."

"We have some really great jewellery – don't you want to see?" Rachel pressed. "Look at this beautiful old locket!"

A flicker of interest crossed Jodie's face. "A locket?" Hanging the dress back on the rail, she crossed to the jewellery case.

Maddy tiptoed invisibly over

to stand next to Rachel. Then, as they looked into the case, both girls gasped. The locket was gone! Maddy felt her blood run cold. Wordlessly Rachel gaped down at the spot where the locket had been. "Er . . ."

"What locket?" said Jodie with a frown.

"No . . . well . . . there *used* to

be one," stammered Rachel. "Just give me a minute – I'm sure I can find it . . ." She reached for the case door, then dropped her hand, looking frustrated. Maddy winced as she remembered – the case was always locked! And Aunt Tilly had the key on her key chain. Even if the locket *was* in there, they wouldn't be able to get it out.

Katie had come over too, and was scanning the case. "There *isn't* any locket," she said decisively. She gave Rachel a sceptical look, and turned away. "Come on, Jodie, you're not really going to buy something from here, are you? Let's go to the shopping centre."

Jodie shook her dark head. "Just a few more minutes!" she said, heading back to the clothes.

Maddy stared down at the case in dismay. Where could the locket have gone? Suddenly she remembered how close to the edge of the shelf it had been when she last saw it. Could it have fallen off the shelf, somehow?

Peering down, she held back a gasp. She could just glimpse the locket's gold chain at the bottom of the cabinet! The locket itself was buried in shadows.

"Down there!" she murmured in Rachel's ear. "See? In the corner."

Rachel nodded tensely, looking worried.

"*Jodie!*" laughed Katie from the clothes rack, tugging at her friend's arm. "Come on!"

Jodie shook her head. "No, not just

yet . . . It's sort of funny; I just have a feeling that there's something in here that I need." She looked around the shop with her eyebrows drawn together.

Maddy's heart leaped. That was just how she herself had felt, before she found the locket! They *had* to get the locket out so Jodie could see it, somehow.

Nibs jumped lightly onto the counter, staring down into the case. "Wait a minute," she muttered suddenly, pacing invisibly back and forth on the glass surface. "There's a sort of gap at the bottom of the cabinet – see? If I can just slip into it . . ."

Hastily Maddy picked up the little cat and put her onto the floor. Nibs scooted away under the cabinet. Peering down, Maddy could just see her a moment later, squeezing her way through a tiny opening at the bottom of the cabinet. She padded quickly over to where the locket was.

Rachel's eyes grew wide as the locket's chain began to move and twitch on its own. "Yes! She's got it!" she whispered loudly, punching the air in triumph.

Katie stared over at her again, looking even more sceptical than before. "This place is weird," she announced to Jodie.

"Aren't you ready to go yet?"

Jodie had left the clothes rack by now, and was wandering around the tables, looking at all the items. "In a minute," she said distantly, examining an old clock. She put it down again, tucking a strand of her long hair back. "Katie, it's the strangest feeling – it's like there's something in here I *have* to have!"

Shaking her head, Katie marched over to her and took her arm. "Come on, I'm saving you from yourself," she said with a grin. "Topshop! Now!"

Jodie hesitated, and then laughed too. "Oh, all right. I suppose I'm just being silly."

"No!" Rachel burst out, springing out from behind the counter. She hurried over to them, blocking their way. "I mean – I mean, don't go just yet. There's still loads you haven't seen!"

The two teenagers stared at her, then at each other. "No, um . . . actually, I think we have to go now," said Jodie, taking a cautious step around her in the direction of the door.

In the cabinet, Nibs was quickly dragging the locket towards the

opening in the corner. Maddy watched anxiously as the little cat pulled the chain through – and then the locket itself got stuck in a narrow part of the gap. Maddy gaped in horror as Nibs twisted and pulled at it – to no avail. *No!*

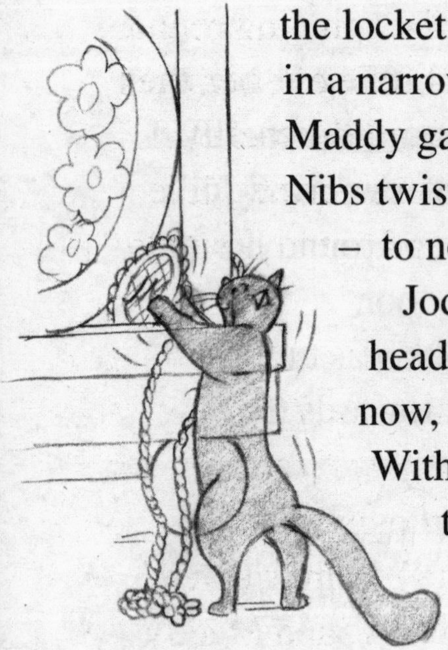

Jodie and Katie were heading across the shop now, almost at the door. With a final sharp tug, the locket popped free, clattering onto the floor.

Nibs appeared from under the counter, dragging the locket after her. Scooping it up, Maddy ran invisibly over to the door. Just as the girls reached for it, she tugged sharply at Jodie's arm – and laid the locket on a table next to the door.

"Oh!" gasped Jodie, spinning round. "What was—" She broke off, her eyes widening as she spotted the locket. "Katie, look at this!" she cried. "It's an old locket – and it's got my initials on it!"

As she picked up the locket, Josephine, still floating near the ceiling, woke abruptly with a snort. Maddy watched as the ghost stared down at Jodie. Slowly a smile spread across her wrinkled face, and Maddy felt her spirits leap. Jodie was the one!

"Hey, how about that?" said Katie. "That's really pretty."

"You know . . ." Jodie trailed off, rubbing her finger on the locket's garnet. "I'm sure I remember Dad mentioning an old family locket once. It got lost or something, when my great-uncle's wife wore it to a party in someone's house. It used to be my great-grandmother's – she was called Josephine."

"You don't suppose this could be it, do you?" gasped Katie.

Just then, Aunt Tilly came back into the shop. "Oh, hello," she said cheerfully to the two girls. "Are you finding everything you—" She broke off, frowning, as she saw the locket. "Why – how did that get out of the case?"

"It wasn't in a case," said Jodie in confusion. "It was right here." She pointed at the table.

Rachel came over to them. "Yes, I

saw them pick it up, Aunt Tilly," she said, looking innocent. "It must have got out of the case somehow."

Maddy grinned to herself. Rachel wasn't lying – it was true, the locket *must* have got out of the case somehow!

"But . . ." Aunt Tilly stared at the case, and then back at the locket. Then she looked nervously around the shop. "Um . . . nothing strange happened when you picked it up, did it?"

Jodie blinked. "Like what?"

"Nothing!" said Aunt Tilly hastily, looking relieved.

"Jodie was just saying that this locket might have belonged to her family," put in Katie. Eagerly the two girls told Aunt Tilly the story.

"And if I'm right, then the photo inside should be of my great-grandmother when she was young," said Jodie. "I think there's supposed to be a lock of her hair there too." Her fingers hovered over the locket's catch. "May I?" she asked, her eyes shining.

Josephine had drifted very close to Jodie, and stood peering over her shoulder, a wide smile on her wrinkled face. Aunt Tilly nodded, and Jodie carefully prised the locket's lid open. There was a photo, and a lock of dark hair. "See, it *is* her!" she cried.

"Whoa . . . she looks just like you," breathed Katie.

Peering invisibly over Jodie's shoulder, Maddy saw that it was true. The young Josephine looked very like

Jodie, with her long hair and large eyes!

"Oh, I must have this!" cried Jodie, clasping the locket to her. "How much is it? I mean I – I know I probably can't afford it, but maybe if I ask my parents—"

Aunt Tilly hesitated, looking around her shop. All at once Maddy knew what she was thinking – the strange upsets seemed to have stopped for now . . . but would they begin again, if the locket stayed? Aunt Tilly glanced back at Jodie, and seemed to make up her mind about something.

"You know what, I think you should just have the locket," she said, closing Jodie's hand around it with a smile. "It belongs to your family, not me."

"*Really?*" gasped Jodie.

Aunt Tilly nodded. "Really!"

Carefully Jodie hung the locket around her neck. It gleamed and winked in the light. "Oh, thank you!" she exclaimed, clutching it tightly. She grinned at her friend. "See, Katie – I *told* you it felt like there was something in here I had to have!"

Katie shook her head. "You're such a witch!" she teased.

A witch. Maddy felt a chill run across her scalp. Perhaps Josephine's powers ran in the family! She glanced at Josephine . . . and saw that the ghost was smiling at her. *Thank you* Josephine mouthed at Maddy, her eyes warm.

As Maddy watched, the ghost slowly faded from view. The last that Maddy saw of her, Josephine was smiling at her great-granddaughter, watching her with pride.

Maddy gave an invisible spin as the two girls left the shop, chatting excitedly. They'd done it! Josephine had been set free of the spell that had tied her to the locket! She felt Nibs scamper up her jeans to her shoulder. "Well done!" whispered the little cat in her ear.

"Where's Maddy?" said Aunt Tilly, glancing around.

"Oh, um – she's around here somewhere," said Rachel.

Ducking behind one of the racks of clothes, Maddy made herself visible again. "I'm here," she said, wandering casually out. Nibs sat curled in her pocket, her tiny body warm and firm. Maddy stroked her with her finger, already dreading the time when the little cat would have to depart.

Aunt Tilly smiled at Maddy. "I can't believe it's almost time for you girls to go home already! It's been an interesting week, hasn't it?" Then she sighed. "I just hope my customers start coming back now that I've got rid of that locket! You know, I almost think that there *was* something strange about it."

Almost the moment the words had left Aunt Tilly's mouth, the shop door jangled and a woman came in. "Is this the haunted antique shop?" she asked eagerly, looking around.

Aunt Tilly's jaw dropped. "Er – well, no, I wouldn't say it was *haunted*, exactly . . ."

"Oh." The woman's face fell. "You mean Clarissa's story wasn't true?"

"Clarissa?" gasped Aunt Tilly. "Oh no, what has she been saying?"

The woman's eyes gleamed. "She's been telling everyone about how she held a séance here, and contacted all the ghosts! Did the books *really* fly off the shelf?"

Aunt Tilly blinked at the woman's enthusiastic tone. "Well, yes, but – there must have been some logical explanation for it . . ."

The door's bell jingled again, and a few more people came in. "Ooh, it's just like Clarissa said!" exclaimed one of them happily. "Isn't it creepy? You can just *feel* the ghostly presences!"

"Now, wait a minute— " started Aunt Tilly, but then she broke off as even more people entered the shop. In no time at all, Aunt Tilly was busy helping customers, and answering questions. "Yes, this is the clock that started going on its own . . . and here's where the glass fell . . . Yes, the locket used to be over there in the jewellery case; it all started when it first came into the shop . . . but there can't *really* be ghosts, you know!" This last fell on deaf ears. The customers wandered happily around the shop, taking photos and looking at the antiques for sale.

"They're all mad," whispered Rachel in Maddy's ear. "I think they *want* there to be ghosts here!"

Maddy nodded, watching as the queue for the till grew. "But at least it looks like Aunt Tilly's shop will be OK," she murmured back with a smile. Everyone wanted a souvenir from the haunted antique shop!

Then her smile faded as she felt Nibs pawing at her through her jeans pocket. She knew what that meant . . . it was almost time for the little cat to leave.

"I've got to, um . . . go upstairs,"

she said to Rachel, struggling to hold back sudden tears.

"Oh no – is it time?" asked Rachel anxiously.

Maddy nodded, and Rachel squeezed her hand. "I'll wait for you down here," she said. Maddy's mother wasn't due to pick them up for another hour or so, and both girls were already packed.

Nodding glumly, Maddy started up the stairs. Though she was very glad that Josephine had been set free, and that Aunt Tilly's shop was going to be all right, this was the part of the magic that she hated . . . having to say goodbye to the cats once they were done.

"You did an excellent job," said Nibs warmly. The tiny cat was sitting on the dressing table beside Maddy's hairbrush. Behind her, Greykin and Ollie both sat waiting, smiles on their ceramic faces. "Dealing with a ghost isn't easy, believe me!" Nibs shuddered, obviously remembering the dampness of her fur, and Maddy

Talc

smiled despite her sorrow.

"Oh, Nibs, I wish you didn't have to go just yet," she sighed, stroking the little cat's back. Nibs purred, rubbing and bumping against her hand.

"I wish that, too," she said. Then she paused, frowning. "But you might see me again sooner than you think."

Maddy's heart leaped. "*Really?* Will you be coming back again next?" Then she stopped, her eyes flying to the ceramic cats. "But – what about Ollie?" It was the long-haired tabby's turn next.

Nibs seemed to shake herself. "I don't know," she said, twitching her black whiskers thoughtfully. "It's just a feeling. But no matter when I see you next, Maddy, you know that I'll be thinking of you. You're rather a lovely human, you know!"

Picking up the tiny cat in her hands, Maddy cuddled her against her cheek, listening to her purr and purr. "I'm going to miss you, Nibs," she whispered, blinking back tears. Sometimes it was months and months between adventures. It might be ages before she saw one of the cats again!

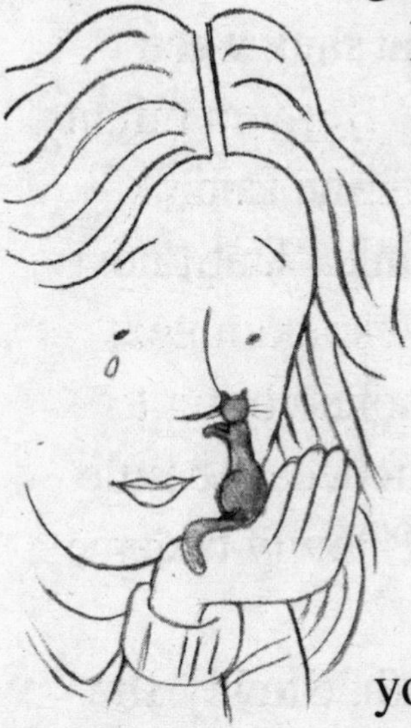

"And I'll miss you," said Nibs, gazing up at her with her emerald-green eyes. Gently she rose up on her hind legs and gave Maddy a cat-kiss, touching her nose to hers. "I'm afraid it's time now," she added.

After a final cuddle, Maddy put Nibs back down on the dressing table, watching sadly as the tiny cat prowled over to Greykin and Ollie. She sat down beside them, carefully arranging her paws and tail so that they were entwined with theirs.

"Goodbye, dear one," she said, closing one eye in a wink. "Until next time!"

"Goodbye, Nibs," choked out Maddy. And as she watched, the little cat shimmered . . . and slowly became ceramic once more.

Maddy let out a breath. Slowly she picked up all three cats, running her finger over their ceramic coolness. She'd never get used to this part of the magic! It was so hard to say goodbye to her feline friends when the time came.

"Goodbye," she murmured again, touching Nibs's nose. Then she remembered what Nibs had said, and a tiny flicker of excitement grew within her. What would her next adventure be? Would she really see Nibs again soon?

"Until next time," she said to the cats, carefully wrapping them back in their silk handkerchief. "And I can hardly wait!"

THE END